C000092374

GOLDEN RETRIEVER LOVER'S ADDRESS BOOK

Published in 2006 by
First Stone Publishing
PO Box 8, Lydney,
Gloucestershire, GL15 6YD UK

© **First Stone Publishing 2006**

ISBN 1 904439 58 6

ACKNOWLEDGEMENTS

The publisher would like to thank Nick Ridley (pages 3, 53) for help with photography.

Photo Credits:
Page 15: © istockphoto.com/Ket Sen Chin
Page 31: © istockphoto.com/Jan Tyler
Page 67: © istockphoto.com/Jan de Wild
Page 99: © istockphoto.com/John Fredericksen
Page 115: © istockphoto.com/PK Photos
Back cover photograph © istockphoto.com/Ket Sen Chin

Printed and bound in China through Printworks International Limited

a

Name

Address

Telephone 1:

Telephone 2:

Email:

Name

Address

Telephone 1:

Telephone 2:

Email:

Name

Address

Telephone 1:

Telephone 2:

Email:

Name

Address

Telephone 1:

Telephone 2:

Email:

Name

Address

Telephone 1:

Telephone 2:

Email:

Name

Address

Telephone 1:

Telephone 2:

Email:

Name

Address

Telephone 1:

Telephone 2:

Email:

Name

Address

Telephone 1:

Telephone 2:

Email:

The Golden Retriever was developed by Lord Tweedsmouth, who was from Guisachan, an extensive shooting estate in Scotland.

Name

Address

Telephone 1:

Telephone 2:

Email:

Name

Address

Telephone 1:

Telephone 2:

Email:

Name

Address

Telephone 1:

Telephone 2:

Email:

Name

Address

Telephone 1:

Telephone 2:

Email:

Name

Address

Telephone 1:

Telephone 2:

Email:

Name

Address

Telephone 1:

Telephone 2:

Email:

Name

Address

Telephone 1:

Telephone 2:

Email:

Name

Address

Telephone 1:

Telephone 2:

Email:

Name

Address

Telephone 1:

Telephone 2:

Email:

Name

Address

Telephone 1:

Telephone 2:

Email:

Name

Address

Telephone 1:

Telephone 2:

Email:

Name

Address

Telephone 1:

Telephone 2:

Email:

Name

Address

Telephone 1:

Telephone 2:

Email:

Name

Address

Telephone 1:

Telephone 2:

Email:

Name

Address

Telephone 1:

Telephone 2:

Email:

Name

Address

Telephone 1:

Telephone 2:

Email:

Name

Address

Telephone 1:

Telephone 2:

Email:

Lord Tweedsmouth bought a yellow retriever from a cobbler after seeing the dog walking through the streets of Brighton.

Name	Name	Name
Address	Address	Address
Telephone 1:	Telephone 1:	Telephone 1:
Telephone 2:	Telephone 2:	Telephone 2:
Email:	Email:	Email:

Name	Name	Name
Address	Address	Address
Telephone 1:	Telephone 1:	Telephone 1:
Telephone 2:	Telephone 2:	Telephone 2:
Email:	Email:	Email:

Name	Name	Name
Address	Address	Address
Telephone 1:	Telephone 1:	Telephone 1:
Telephone 2:	Telephone 2:	Telephone 2:
Email:	Email:	Email:

Name

Address

Telephone 1:

Telephone 2:

Email:

Name

Address

Telephone 1:

Telephone 2:

Email:

Name

Address

Telephone 1:

Telephone 2:

Email:

Name

Address

Telephone 1:

Telephone 2:

Email:

Name

Address

Telephone 1:

Telephone 2:

Email:

Name

Address

Telephone 1:

Telephone 2:

Email:

Name

Address

Telephone 1:

Telephone 2:

Email:

Name

Address

Telephone 1:

Telephone 2:

Email:

Name

Address

Telephone 1:

Telephone 2:

Email:

b

Name

Address

Telephone 1:

Telephone 2:

Email:

Name

Address

Telephone 1:

Telephone 2:

Email:

Name

Address

Telephone 1:

Telephone 2:

Email:

Name

Address

Telephone 1:

Telephone 2:

Email:

Name

Address

Telephone 1:

Telephone 2:

Email:

Name

Address

Telephone 1:

Telephone 2:

Email:

Name

Address

Telephone 1:

Telephone 2:

Email:

Name

Address

Telephone 1:

Telephone 2:

Email:

Lord Tweedsmouth
named the dog Nous
(Gaelic for 'wisdom').
Nous was the only yellow
dog in a litter of black,
wavy-coated puppies.

Name	Name	Name
Address	Address	Address
Telephone 1:	Telephone 1:	Telephone 1:
Telephone 2:	Telephone 2:	Telephone 2:
Email:	Email:	Email:

Name	Name	Name
Address	Address	Address
Telephone 1:	Telephone 1:	Telephone 1:
Telephone 2:	Telephone 2:	Telephone 2:
Email:	Email:	Email:

Name	Name	Name
Address	Address	Address
Telephone 1:	Telephone 1:	Telephone 1:
Telephone 2:	Telephone 2:	Telephone 2:
Email:	Email:	Email:

Name

Address

Telephone 1:

Telephone 2:

Email:

Name

Address

Telephone 1:

Telephone 2:

Email:

Name

Address

Telephone 1:

Telephone 2:

Email:

Name

Address

Telephone 1:

Telephone 2:

Email:

Name

Address

Telephone 1:

Telephone 2:

Email:

Name

Address

Telephone 1:

Telephone 2:

Email:

Name

Address

Telephone 1:

Telephone 2:

Email:

Name

Address

Telephone 1:

Telephone 2:

Email:

Lord Tweedsmouth was so impressed by the way his dog Nous retrieved birds, that he decided to start his own line of retrievers.

Name

Address

Telephone 1:

Telephone 2:

Email:

Name

Address

Telephone 1:

Telephone 2:

Email:

Name

Address

Telephone 1:

Telephone 2:

Email:

Name

Address

Telephone 1:

Telephone 2:

Email:

Name

Address

Telephone 1:

Telephone 2:

Email:

Name

Address

Telephone 1:

Telephone 2:

Email:

Name

Address

Telephone 1:

Telephone 2:

Email:

Name

Address

Telephone 1:

Telephone 2:

Email:

Name

Address

Telephone 1:

Telephone 2:

Email:

Name	Name	Name
Address	Address	Address
Telephone 1:	Telephone 1:	Telephone 1:
Telephone 2:	Telephone 2:	Telephone 2:
Email:	Email:	Email:

Name	Name	Name
Address	Address	Address
Telephone 1:	Telephone 1:	Telephone 1:
Telephone 2:	Telephone 2:	Telephone 2:
Email:	Email:	Email:

Name	Name	Name
Address	Address	Address
Telephone 1:	Telephone 1:	Telephone 1:
Telephone 2:	Telephone 2:	Telephone 2:
Email:	Email:	Email:

C

Name

Address

Telephone 1:

Telephone 2:

Email:

Name

Address

Telephone 1:

Telephone 2:

Email:

Name

Address

Telephone 1:

Telephone 2:

Email:

Name

Address

Telephone 1:

Telephone 2:

Email:

Name

Address

Telephone 1:

Telephone 2:

Email:

Name

Address

Telephone 1:

Telephone 2:

Email:

Name

Address

Telephone 1:

Telephone 2:

Email:

Name

Address

Telephone 1:

Telephone 2:

Email:

In 1868 Nous mated with Belle, a Tweed Water Spaniel. The litter contained three yellow puppies – the foundation of the Golden Retriever breed.

Name	Name	Name
Address	Address	Address
Telephone 1:	Telephone 1:	Telephone 1:
Telephone 2:	Telephone 2:	Telephone 2:
Email:	Email:	Email:

Name	Name	Name
Address	Address	Address
Telephone 1:	Telephone 1:	Telephone 1:
Telephone 2:	Telephone 2:	Telephone 2:
Email:	Email:	Email:

Name	Name	Name
Address	Address	Address
Telephone 1:	Telephone 1:	Telephone 1:
Telephone 2:	Telephone 2:	Telephone 2:
Email:	Email:	Email:

Name	Name	Name
Address	Address	Address
Telephone 1:	Telephone 1:	Telephone 1:
Telephone 2:	Telephone 2:	Telephone 2:
Email:	Email:	Email:

Name	Name	Name
Address	Address	Address
Telephone 1:	Telephone 1:	Telephone 1:
Telephone 2:	Telephone 2:	Telephone 2:
Email:	Email:	Email:

Name	Name
Address	Address
Telephone 1:	Telephone 1:
Telephone 2:	Telephone 2:
Email:	Email:

Lord Tweedsmouth kept meticulous Stud Book records, detailing all the matings and puppies produced in his kennel. This gives us a unique record.

Name

Address

Telephone 1:

Telephone 2:

Email:

Name

Address

Telephone 1:

Telephone 2:

Email:

Name

Address

Telephone 1:

Telephone 2:

Email:

Name

Address

Telephone 1:

Telephone 2:

Email:

Name

Address

Telephone 1:

Telephone 2:

Email:

Name

Address

Telephone 1:

Telephone 2:

Email:

Name

Address

Telephone 1:

Telephone 2:

Email:

Name

Address

Telephone 1:

Telephone 2:

Email:

Name

Address

Telephone 1:

Telephone 2:

Email:

Name

Address

Telephone 1:

Telephone 2:

Email:

Name

Address

Telephone 1:

Telephone 2:

Email:

Name

Address

Telephone 1:

Telephone 2:

Email:

Name

Address

Telephone 1:

Telephone 2:

Email:

Name

Address

Telephone 1:

Telephone 2:

Email:

Name

Address

Telephone 1:

Telephone 2:

Email:

Name

Address

Telephone 1:

Telephone 2:

Email:

Name

Address

Telephone 1:

Telephone 2:

Email:

Name

Address

Telephone 1:

Telephone 2:

Email:

d

Name

Address

Telephone 1:

Telephone 2:

Email:

Name

Address

Telephone 1:

Telephone 2:

Email:

Name

Address

Telephone 1:

Telephone 2:

Email:

Name

Address

Telephone 1:

Telephone 2:

Email:

Name

Address

Telephone 1:

Telephone 2:

Email:

Name

Address

Telephone 1:

Telephone 2:

Email:

Name

Address

Telephone 1:

Telephone 2:

Email:

Name

Address

Telephone 1:

Telephone 2:

Email:

In 1872 Nous and Belle had a second litter, and a yellow-coloured bitch called Ada was given to the fifth Earl of Ilchester.

Name

Address

Telephone 1:

Telephone 2:

Email:

Name

Address

Telephone 1:

Telephone 2:

Email:

Name

Address

Telephone 1:

Telephone 2:

Email:

Name

Address

Telephone 1:

Telephone 2:

Email:

Name

Address

Telephone 1:

Telephone 2:

Email:

Name

Address

Telephone 1:

Telephone 2:

Email:

Name

Address

Telephone 1:

Telephone 2:

Email:

Name

Address

Telephone 1:

Telephone 2:

Email:

Name

Address

Telephone 1:

Telephone 2:

Email:

Name	Name	Name
Address	Address	Address
Telephone 1:	Telephone 1:	Telephone 1:
Telephone 2:	Telephone 2:	Telephone 2:
Email:	Email:	Email:

Name	Name	Name
Address	Address	Address
Telephone 1:	Telephone 1:	Telephone 1:
Telephone 2:	Telephone 2:	Telephone 2:
Email:	Email:	Email:

Name	Name
Address	Address
Telephone 1:	Telephone 1:
Telephone 2:	Telephone 2:
Email:	Email:

Ada was the foundation for the Earl of Ilchester's Melbury kennels. Ada died in 1882 and was buried with a gravestone inscribed 'Ada – With The Golden Hair'.

Name

Address

Telephone 1:

Telephone 2:

Email:

Name

Address

Telephone 1:

Telephone 2:

Email:

Name

Address

Telephone 1:

Telephone 2:

Email:

Name

Address

Telephone 1:

Telephone 2:

Email:

Name

Address

Telephone 1:

Telephone 2:

Email:

Name

Address

Telephone 1:

Telephone 2:

Email:

Name

Address

Telephone 1:

Telephone 2:

Email:

Name

Address

Telephone 1:

Telephone 2:

Email:

Name

Address

Telephone 1:

Telephone 2:

Email:

Name

Address

Telephone 1:

Telephone 2:

Email:

Name

Address

Telephone 1:

Telephone 2:

Email:

Name

Address

Telephone 1:

Telephone 2:

Email:

Name

Address

Telephone 1:

Telephone 2:

Email:

Name

Address

Telephone 1:

Telephone 2:

Email:

Name

Address

Telephone 1:

Telephone 2:

Email:

Name

Address

Telephone 1:

Telephone 2:

Email:

Name

Address

Telephone 1:

Telephone 2:

Email:

Name

Address

Telephone 1:

Telephone 2:

Email:

e

Name

Address

Telephone 1:

Telephone 2:

Email:

Name

Address

Telephone 1:

Telephone 2:

Email:

Name

Address

Telephone 1:

Telephone 2:

Email:

Name

Address

Telephone 1:

Telephone 2:

Email:

Name

Address

Telephone 1:

Telephone 2:

Email:

Name

Address

Telephone 1:

Telephone 2:

Email:

Name

Address

Telephone 1:

Telephone 2:

Email:

Name

Address

Telephone 1:

Telephone 2:

Email:

There was a theory, now discounted, that Lord Tweedsmouth bought his first retrievers from a troupe of Russian circus dogs.

Name	Name	Name
Address	Address	Address
Telephone 1:	Telephone 1:	Telephone 1:
Telephone 2:	Telephone 2:	Telephone 2:
Email:	Email:	Email:

Name	Name	Name
Address	Address	Address
Telephone 1:	Telephone 1:	Telephone 1:
Telephone 2:	Telephone 2:	Telephone 2:
Email:	Email:	Email:

Name	Name	Name
Address	Address	Address
Telephone 1:	Telephone 1:	Telephone 1:
Telephone 2:	Telephone 2:	Telephone 2:
Email:	Email:	Email:

Name	Name	Name
Address	Address	Address
Telephone 1:	Telephone 1:	Telephone 1:
Telephone 2:	Telephone 2:	Telephone 2:
Email:	Email:	Email:

Name	Name	Name
Address	Address	Address
Telephone 1:	Telephone 1:	Telephone 1:
Telephone 2:	Telephone 2:	Telephone 2:
Email:	Email:	Email:

Name	Name	Name
Address	Address	Address
Telephone 1:	Telephone 1:	Telephone 1:
Telephone 2:	Telephone 2:	Telephone 2:
Email:	Email:	Email:

Name		Name		Name
Address		Address		Address
Telephone 1:		Telephone 1:		Telephone 1:
Telephone 2:		Telephone 2:		Telephone 2:
Email:		Email:		Email:

Name		Name		Name
Address		Address		Address
Telephone 1:		Telephone 1:		Telephone 1:
Telephone 2:		Telephone 2:		Telephone 2:
Email:		Email:		Email:

Name		Name
Address		Address
Telephone 1:		Telephone 1:
Telephone 2:		Telephone 2:
Email:		Email:

Setters and different types of retrievers were used in early breeding programmes. It was found that mating a black dog and a yellow bitch produced yellow puppies.

Name	Name	Name
Address	Address	Address
Telephone 1:	Telephone 1:	Telephone 1:
Telephone 2:	Telephone 2:	Telephone 2:
Email:	Email:	Email:

Name	Name	Name
Address	Address	Address
Telephone 1:	Telephone 1:	Telephone 1:
Telephone 2:	Telephone 2:	Telephone 2:
Email:	Email:	Email:

Name	Name	Name
Address	Address	Address
Telephone 1:	Telephone 1:	Telephone 1:
Telephone 2:	Telephone 2:	Telephone 2:
Email:	Email:	Email:

Name

Address

Telephone 1:

Telephone 2:

Email:

Name

Address

Telephone 1:

Telephone 2:

Email:

Name

Address

Telephone 1:

Telephone 2:

Email:

Name

Address

Telephone 1:

Telephone 2:

Email:

Name

Address

Telephone 1:

Telephone 2:

Email:

Name

Address

Telephone 1:

Telephone 2:

Email:

Name

Address

Telephone 1:

Telephone 2:

Email:

Name

Address

Telephone 1:

Telephone 2:

Email:

In the 1890s, a sandy coloured Bloodhound was mated with a retriever to improve the Golden's scenting ability.

Name	Name	Name
Address	Address	Address
Telephone 1:	Telephone 1:	Telephone 1:
Telephone 2:	Telephone 2:	Telephone 2:
Email:	Email:	Email:

Name	Name	Name
Address	Address	Address
Telephone 1:	Telephone 1:	Telephone 1:
Telephone 2:	Telephone 2:	Telephone 2:
Email:	Email:	Email:

Name	Name	Name
Address	Address	Address
Telephone 1:	Telephone 1:	Telephone 1:
Telephone 2:	Telephone 2:	Telephone 2:
Email:	Email:	Email:

Name

Address

Telephone 1:

Telephone 2:

Email:

Name

Address

Telephone 1:

Telephone 2:

Email:

Name

Address

Telephone 1:

Telephone 2:

Email:

Name

Address

Telephone 1:

Telephone 2:

Email:

Name

Address

Telephone 1:

Telephone 2:

Email:

Name

Address

Telephone 1:

Telephone 2:

Email:

Name

Address

Telephone 1:

Telephone 2:

Email:

Name

Address

Telephone 1:

Telephone 2:

Email:

Name

Address

Telephone 1:

Telephone 2:

Email:

Name

Address

Telephone 1:

Telephone 2:

Email:

Name

Address

Telephone 1:

Telephone 2:

Email:

Name

Address

Telephone 1:

Telephone 2:

Email:

Name

Address

Telephone 1:

Telephone 2:

Email:

Name

Address

Telephone 1:

Telephone 2:

Email:

Name

Address

Telephone 1:

Telephone 2:

Email:

Name

Address

Telephone 1:

Telephone 2:

Email:

When Golden Retrievers were being developed as top-class gundogs, Lord de Grey calculated that between 1867 and 1923 he shot 500,000 game birds.

Name	Name	Name
Address	Address	Address
Telephone 1:	Telephone 1:	Telephone 1:
Telephone 2:	Telephone 2:	Telephone 2:
Email:	Email:	Email:

Name	Name	Name
Address	Address	Address
Telephone 1:	Telephone 1:	Telephone 1:
Telephone 2:	Telephone 2:	Telephone 2:
Email:	Email:	Email:

Name	Name	Name
Address	Address	Address
Telephone 1:	Telephone 1:	Telephone 1:
Telephone 2:	Telephone 2:	Telephone 2:
Email:	Email:	Email:

Name

Address

Telephone 1:

Telephone 2:

Email:

Name

Address

Telephone 1:

Telephone 2:

Email:

Name

Address

Telephone 1:

Telephone 2:

Email:

Name

Address

Telephone 1:

Telephone 2:

Email:

Name

Address

Telephone 1:

Telephone 2:

Email:

Name

Address

Telephone 1:

Telephone 2:

Email:

Name

Address

Telephone 1:

Telephone 2:

Email:

Name

Address

Telephone 1:

Telephone 2:

Email:

In the 1880s, Archie Marjoribanks, youngest son of Lord Tweedsmouth, went to America. He took two retrievers, Lady and Sol, to start the breed in the USA.

Name	Name	Name
Address	Address	Address
Telephone 1:	Telephone 1:	Telephone 1:
Telephone 2:	Telephone 2:	Telephone 2:
Email:	Email:	Email:

Name	Name	Name
Address	Address	Address
Telephone 1:	Telephone 1:	Telephone 1:
Telephone 2:	Telephone 2:	Telephone 2:
Email:	Email:	Email:

Name	Name	Name
Address	Address	Address
Telephone 1:	Telephone 1:	Telephone 1:
Telephone 2:	Telephone 2:	Telephone 2:
Email:	Email:	Email:

Name

Address

Telephone 1:

Telephone 2:

Email:

Name

Address

Telephone 1:

Telephone 2:

Email:

Name

Address

Telephone 1:

Telephone 2:

Email:

Name

Address

Telephone 1:

Telephone 2:

Email:

Name

Address

Telephone 1:

Telephone 2:

Email:

Name

Address

Telephone 1:

Telephone 2:

Email:

Name

Address

Telephone 1:

Telephone 2:

Email:

Name

Address

Telephone 1:

Telephone 2:

Email:

Name

Address

Telephone 1:

Telephone 2:

Email:

h

Name	Name	Name
Address	Address	Address
Telephone 1:	Telephone 1:	Telephone 1:
Telephone 2:	Telephone 2:	Telephone 2:
Email:	Email:	Email:

Name	Name	Name
Address	Address	Address
Telephone 1:	Telephone 1:	Telephone 1:
Telephone 2:	Telephone 2:	Telephone 2:
Email:	Email:	Email:

	Name	Name
	Address	Address
	Telephone 1:	Telephone 1:
	Telephone 2:	Telephone 2:
	Email:	Email:

In 1908, the first Golden Retrievers – entered as Flat- or Wavy-coated Retrievers – were exhibited at Crufts and Crystal Palace.

Name	Name	Name
Address	Address	Address
Telephone 1:	Telephone 1:	Telephone 1:
Telephone 2:	Telephone 2:	Telephone 2:
Email:	Email:	Email:

Name	Name	Name
Address	Address	Address
Telephone 1:	Telephone 1:	Telephone 1:
Telephone 2:	Telephone 2:	Telephone 2:
Email:	Email:	Email:

Name	Name	Name
Address	Address	Address
Telephone 1:	Telephone 1:	Telephone 1:
Telephone 2:	Telephone 2:	Telephone 2:
Email:	Email:	Email:

Name

Address

Telephone 1:

Telephone 2:

Email:

Name

Address

Telephone 1:

Telephone 2:

Email:

Name

Address

Telephone 1:

Telephone 2:

Email:

Name

Address

Telephone 1:

Telephone 2:

Email:

Name

Address

Telephone 1:

Telephone 2:

Email:

Name

Address

Telephone 1:

Telephone 2:

Email:

Name

Address

Telephone 1:

Telephone 2:

Email:

Name

Address

Telephone 1:

Telephone 2:

Email:

The Kennel Club in England recognised 'Retrievers (Golden, Yellow)' in 1913. It was not until 1920 that the breed was given its present name.

Name	Name	Name
Address	Address	Address
Telephone 1:	Telephone 1:	Telephone 1:
Telephone 2:	Telephone 2:	Telephone 2:
Email:	Email:	Email:

Name	Name	Name
Address	Address	Address
Telephone 1:	Telephone 1:	Telephone 1:
Telephone 2:	Telephone 2:	Telephone 2:
Email:	Email:	Email:

Name	Name	Name
Address	Address	Address
Telephone 1:	Telephone 1:	Telephone 1:
Telephone 2:	Telephone 2:	Telephone 2:
Email:	Email:	Email:

Name	Name	Name
Address	Address	Address
Telephone 1:	Telephone 1:	Telephone 1:
Telephone 2:	Telephone 2:	Telephone 2:
Email:	Email:	Email:

Name	Name	Name
Address	Address	Address
Telephone 1:	Telephone 1:	Telephone 1:
Telephone 2:	Telephone 2:	Telephone 2:
Email:	Email:	Email:

Name	Name	Name
Address	Address	Address
Telephone 1:	Telephone 1:	Telephone 1:
Telephone 2:	Telephone 2:	Telephone 2:
Email:	Email:	Email:

i

Name

Address

Telephone 1:

Telephone 2:

Email:

Name

Address

Telephone 1:

Telephone 2:

Email:

Name

Address

Telephone 1:

Telephone 2:

Email:

Name

Address

Telephone 1:

Telephone 2:

Email:

Name

Address

Telephone 1:

Telephone 2:

Email:

Name

Address

Telephone 1:

Telephone 2:

Email:

Name

Address

Telephone 1:

Telephone 2:

Email:

Name

Address

Telephone 1:

Telephone 2:

Email:

One of the most important early pioneers of the breed was Winifred Maud Charlesworth of the Noranby kennels.

Name

Address

Telephone 1:

Telephone 2:

Email:

Name

Address

Telephone 1:

Telephone 2:

Email:

Name

Address

Telephone 1:

Telephone 2:

Email:

Name

Address

Telephone 1:

Telephone 2:

Email:

Name

Address

Telephone 1:

Telephone 2:

Email:

Name

Address

Telephone 1:

Telephone 2:

Email:

Name

Address

Telephone 1:

Telephone 2:

Email:

Name

Address

Telephone 1:

Telephone 2:

Email:

Name

Address

Telephone 1:

Telephone 2:

Email:

Name	Name	Name
Address	Address	Address
Telephone 1:	Telephone 1:	Telephone 1:
Telephone 2:	Telephone 2:	Telephone 2:
Email:	Email:	Email:
Name	Name	Name
Address	Address	Address
Telephone 1:	Telephone 1:	Telephone 1:
Telephone 2:	Telephone 2:	Telephone 2:
Email:	Email:	Email:
Name	Name	Name
Address	Address	Address
Telephone 1:	Telephone 1:	Telephone 1:
Telephone 2:	Telephone 2:	Telephone 2:
Email:	Email:	Email:

j

Name

Address

Telephone 1:

Telephone 2:

Email:

Name

Address

Telephone 1:

Telephone 2:

Email:

Name

Address

Telephone 1:

Telephone 2:

Email:

Name

Address

Telephone 1:

Telephone 2:

Email:

Name

Address

Telephone 1:

Telephone 2:

Email:

Name

Address

Telephone 1:

Telephone 2:

Email:

Name

Address

Telephone 1:

Telephone 2:

Email:

Name

Address

Telephone 1:

Telephone 2:

Email:

The first Golden Retriever to become a Champion was Noranby Campfire, owned by Winifred Maud Charlesworth.

Name

Address

Telephone 1:

Telephone 2:

Email:

Name

Address

Telephone 1:

Telephone 2:

Email:

Name

Address

Telephone 1:

Telephone 2:

Email:

Name

Address

Telephone 1:

Telephone 2:

Email:

Name

Address

Telephone 1:

Telephone 2:

Email:

Name

Address

Telephone 1:

Telephone 2:

Email:

Name

Address

Telephone 1:

Telephone 2:

Email:

Name

Address

Telephone 1:

Telephone 2:

Email:

Name

Address

Telephone 1:

Telephone 2:

Email:

Name

Address

Telephone 1:

Telephone 2:

Email:

Name

Address

Telephone 1:

Telephone 2:

Email:

Name

Address

Telephone 1:

Telephone 2:

Email:

Name

Address

Telephone 1:

Telephone 2:

Email:

Name

Address

Telephone 1:

Telephone 2:

Email:

Name

Address

Telephone 1:

Telephone 2:

Email:

Name

Address

Telephone 1:

Telephone 2:

Email:

Name

Address

Telephone 1:

Telephone 2:

Email:

Name

Address

Telephone 1:

Telephone 2:

Email:

k

Name	Name	Name
Address	Address	Address
Telephone 1:	Telephone 1:	Telephone 1:
Telephone 2:	Telephone 2:	Telephone 2:
Email:	Email:	Email:

Name	Name	Name
Address	Address	Address
Telephone 1:	Telephone 1:	Telephone 1:
Telephone 2:	Telephone 2:	Telephone 2:
Email:	Email:	Email:

	Name	Name
	Address	Address
	Telephone 1:	Telephone 1:
	Telephone 2:	Telephone 2:
	Email:	Email:

The American Kennel Club gave official recognition to the Golden Retriever in 1932.

Name	Name	Name
Address	Address	Address
Telephone 1:	Telephone 1:	Telephone 1:
Telephone 2:	Telephone 2:	Telephone 2:
Email:	Email:	Email:

Name	Name	Name
Address	Address	Address
Telephone 1:	Telephone 1:	Telephone 1:
Telephone 2:	Telephone 2:	Telephone 2:
Email:	Email:	Email:

Name	Name	Name
Address	Address	Address
Telephone 1:	Telephone 1:	Telephone 1:
Telephone 2:	Telephone 2:	Telephone 2:
Email:	Email:	Email:

Name	Name	Name
Address	Address	Address
Telephone 1:	Telephone 1:	Telephone 1:
Telephone 2:	Telephone 2:	Telephone 2:
Email:	Email:	Email:

Name	Name	Name
Address	Address	Address
Telephone 1:	Telephone 1:	Telephone 1:
Telephone 2:	Telephone 2:	Telephone 2:
Email:	Email:	Email:

Name	Name	Name
Address	Address	Address
Telephone 1:	Telephone 1:	Telephone 1:
Telephone 2:	Telephone 2:	Telephone 2:
Email:	Email:	Email:

Name	Name	Name
Address	Address	Address
Telephone 1:	Telephone 1:	Telephone 1:
Telephone 2:	Telephone 2:	Telephone 2:
Email:	Email:	Email:

Name	Name	Name
Address	Address	Address
Telephone 1:	Telephone 1:	Telephone 1:
Telephone 2:	Telephone 2:	Telephone 2:
Email:	Email:	Email:

Name	Name
Address	Address
Telephone 1:	Telephone 1:
Telephone 2:	Telephone 2:
Email:	Email:

The first Golden Retriever Champion in the USA was Am. Can. Ch. Speedwell Pluto. Imported from Britain, he became a highly influential stud dog.

Name	Name	Name
Address	Address	Address
Telephone 1:	Telephone 1:	Telephone 1:
Telephone 2:	Telephone 2:	Telephone 2:
Email:	Email:	Email:

Name	Name	Name
Address	Address	Address
Telephone 1:	Telephone 1:	Telephone 1:
Telephone 2:	Telephone 2:	Telephone 2:
Email:	Email:	Email:

Name	Name	Name
Address	Address	Address
Telephone 1:	Telephone 1:	Telephone 1:
Telephone 2:	Telephone 2:	Telephone 2:
Email:	Email:	Email:

Name		Name		Name	
Address		Address		Address	
Telephone 1:		Telephone 1:		Telephone 1:	
Telephone 2:		Telephone 2:		Telephone 2:	
Email:		Email:		Email:	

Name		Name		Name	
Address		Address		Address	
Telephone 1:		Telephone 1:		Telephone 1:	
Telephone 2:		Telephone 2:		Telephone 2:	
Email:		Email:		Email:	

Name		Name	
Address		Address	
Telephone 1:		Telephone 1:	
Telephone 2:		Telephone 2:	
Email:		Email:	

In the 1930s one of the most important British stud dogs was Michel Of Moreton, with a stud fee of 25 guineas – a huge amount of money at the time.

Name

Address

Telephone 1:

Telephone 2:

Email:

Name

Address

Telephone 1:

Telephone 2:

Email:

Name

Address

Telephone 1:

Telephone 2:

Email:

Name

Address

Telephone 1:

Telephone 2:

Email:

Name

Address

Telephone 1:

Telephone 2:

Email:

Name

Address

Telephone 1:

Telephone 2:

Email:

Name

Address

Telephone 1:

Telephone 2:

Email:

Name

Address

Telephone 1:

Telephone 2:

Email:

Name

Address

Telephone 1:

Telephone 2:

Email:

Name	Name	Name
Address	Address	Address
Telephone 1:	Telephone 1:	Telephone 1:
Telephone 2:	Telephone 2:	Telephone 2:
Email:	Email:	Email:

Name	Name	Name
Address	Address	Address
Telephone 1:	Telephone 1:	Telephone 1:
Telephone 2:	Telephone 2:	Telephone 2:
Email:	Email:	Email:

Name	Name	Name
Address	Address	Address
Telephone 1:	Telephone 1:	Telephone 1:
Telephone 2:	Telephone 2:	Telephone 2:
Email:	Email:	Email:

m

Name

Address

Telephone 1:

Telephone 2:

Email:

Name

Address

Telephone 1:

Telephone 2:

Email:

Name

Address

Telephone 1:

Telephone 2:

Email:

Name

Address

Telephone 1:

Telephone 2:

Email:

Name

Address

Telephone 1:

Telephone 2:

Email:

Name

Address

Telephone 1:

Telephone 2:

Email:

Name

Address

Telephone 1:

Telephone 2:

Email:

Name

Address

Telephone 1:

Telephone 2:

Email:

"What we have in the Golden Retriever is a grand hunting dog... and the best companion imaginable." Sam Magoffin, Amercian breeder, 1938.

Name	Name	Name
Address	Address	Address
Telephone 1:	Telephone 1:	Telephone 1:
Telephone 2:	Telephone 2:	Telephone 2:
Email:	Email:	Email:

Name	Name	Name
Address	Address	Address
Telephone 1:	Telephone 1:	Telephone 1:
Telephone 2:	Telephone 2:	Telephone 2:
Email:	Email:	Email:

Name	Name	Name
Address	Address	Address
Telephone 1:	Telephone 1:	Telephone 1:
Telephone 2:	Telephone 2:	Telephone 2:
Email:	Email:	Email:

m

Name

Address

Telephone 1:

Telephone 2:

Email:

Name

Address

Telephone 1:

Telephone 2:

Email:

Name

Address

Telephone 1:

Telephone 2:

Email:

Name

Address

Telephone 1:

Telephone 2:

Email:

Name

Address

Telephone 1:

Telephone 2:

Email:

Name

Address

Telephone 1:

Telephone 2:

Email:

Name

Address

Telephone 1:

Telephone 2:

Email:

Name

Address

Telephone 1:

Telephone 2:

Email:

The Golden Retriever likes to work closely with its handler. The breed is known for its excellent scenting ability, and its soft mouth that delivers game intact.

Name	Name	Name
Address	Address	Address
Telephone 1:	Telephone 1:	Telephone 1:
Telephone 2:	Telephone 2:	Telephone 2:
Email:	Email:	Email:

Name	Name	Name
Address	Address	Address
Telephone 1:	Telephone 1:	Telephone 1:
Telephone 2:	Telephone 2:	Telephone 2:
Email:	Email:	Email:

Name	Name	Name
Address	Address	Address
Telephone 1:	Telephone 1:	Telephone 1:
Telephone 2:	Telephone 2:	Telephone 2:
Email:	Email:	Email:

Name

Address

Telephone 1:

Telephone 2:

Email:

Name

Address

Telephone 1:

Telephone 2:

Email:

Name

Address

Telephone 1:

Telephone 2:

Email:

Name

Address

Telephone 1:

Telephone 2:

Email:

Name

Address

Telephone 1:

Telephone 2:

Email:

Name

Address

Telephone 1:

Telephone 2:

Email:

Name

Address

Telephone 1:

Telephone 2:

Email:

Name

Address

Telephone 1:

Telephone 2:

Email:

Name

Address

Telephone 1:

Telephone 2:

Email:

n

Name	Name	Name
Address	Address	Address
Telephone 1:	Telephone 1:	Telephone 1:
Telephone 2:	Telephone 2:	Telephone 2:
Email:	Email:	Email:

Name	Name	Name
Address	Address	Address
Telephone 1:	Telephone 1:	Telephone 1:
Telephone 2:	Telephone 2:	Telephone 2:
Email:	Email:	Email:

	Name	Name
	Address	Address
	Telephone 1:	Telephone 1:
	Telephone 2:	Telephone 2:
	Email:	Email:

Golden Retrievers bred for showing tend to be bigger boned, longer and heavier. Field-bred Goldens are smaller, longer in the leg and a red-gold colour.

Name

Address

Telephone 1:

Telephone 2:

Email:

Name

Address

Telephone 1:

Telephone 2:

Email:

Name

Address

Telephone 1:

Telephone 2:

Email:

Name

Address

Telephone 1:

Telephone 2:

Email:

Name

Address

Telephone 1:

Telephone 2:

Email:

Name

Address

Telephone 1:

Telephone 2:

Email:

Name

Address

Telephone 1:

Telephone 2:

Email:

Name

Address

Telephone 1:

Telephone 2:

Email:

Name

Address

Telephone 1:

Telephone 2:

Email:

Name	Name	Name
Address	Address	Address
Telephone 1:	Telephone 1:	Telephone 1:
Telephone 2:	Telephone 2:	Telephone 2:
Email:	Email:	Email:

Name	Name	Name
Address	Address	Address
Telephone 1:	Telephone 1:	Telephone 1:
Telephone 2:	Telephone 2:	Telephone 2:
Email:	Email:	Email:

Name	Name
Address	Address
Telephone 1:	Telephone 1:
Telephone 2:	Telephone 2:
Email:	Email:

The highest distinction for a gundog is to be a dual Champion of field and show ring. The last Golden Retriever dual Champion was David of Westley, born in 1951.

Name	Name	Name
Address	Address	Address
Telephone 1:	Telephone 1:	Telephone 1:
Telephone 2:	Telephone 2:	Telephone 2:
Email:	Email:	Email:

Name	Name	Name
Address	Address	Address
Telephone 1:	Telephone 1:	Telephone 1:
Telephone 2:	Telephone 2:	Telephone 2:
Email:	Email:	Email:

Name	Name	Name
Address	Address	Address
Telephone 1:	Telephone 1:	Telephone 1:
Telephone 2:	Telephone 2:	Telephone 2:
Email:	Email:	Email:

Name

Address

Telephone 1:

Telephone 2:

Email:

Name

Address

Telephone 1:

Telephone 2:

Email:

Name

Address

Telephone 1:

Telephone 2:

Email:

Name

Address

Telephone 1:

Telephone 2:

Email:

Name

Address

Telephone 1:

Telephone 2:

Email:

Name

Address

Telephone 1:

Telephone 2:

Email:

Name

Address

Telephone 1:

Telephone 2:

Email:

Name

Address

Telephone 1:

Telephone 2:

Email:

Name

Address

Telephone 1:

Telephone 2:

Email:

o

Name

Address

Telephone 1:

Telephone 2:

Email:

Name

Address

Telephone 1:

Telephone 2:

Email:

Name

Address

Telephone 1:

Telephone 2:

Email:

Name

Address

Telephone 1:

Telephone 2:

Email:

Name

Address

Telephone 1:

Telephone 2:

Email:

Name

Address

Telephone 1:

Telephone 2:

Email:

Name

Address

Telephone 1:

Telephone 2:

Email:

Name

Address

Telephone 1:

Telephone 2:

Email:

Gerald Ford, President of the USA (1974-1977), owned a Golden Retriever called Liberty while he was living in the White House.

Name	Name	Name
Address	Address	Address
Telephone 1:	Telephone 1:	Telephone 1:
Telephone 2:	Telephone 2:	Telephone 2:
Email:	Email:	Email:

Name	Name	Name
Address	Address	Address
Telephone 1:	Telephone 1:	Telephone 1:
Telephone 2:	Telephone 2:	Telephone 2:
Email:	Email:	Email:

Name	Name	Name
Address	Address	Address
Telephone 1:	Telephone 1:	Telephone 1:
Telephone 2:	Telephone 2:	Telephone 2:
Email:	Email:	Email:

Name	Name	Name
Address	Address	Address
Telephone 1:	Telephone 1:	Telephone 1:
Telephone 2:	Telephone 2:	Telephone 2:
Email:	Email:	Email:

Name	Name	Name
Address	Address	Address
Telephone 1:	Telephone 1:	Telephone 1:
Telephone 2:	Telephone 2:	Telephone 2:
Email:	Email:	Email:

Name	Name	Name
Address	Address	Address
Telephone 1:	Telephone 1:	Telephone 1:
Telephone 2:	Telephone 2:	Telephone 2:
Email:	Email:	Email:

p

Name	Name	Name
Address	Address	Address
Telephone 1:	Telephone 1:	Telephone 1:
Telephone 2:	Telephone 2:	Telephone 2:
Email:	Email:	Email:

Name	Name	Name
Address	Address	Address
Telephone 1:	Telephone 1:	Telephone 1:
Telephone 2:	Telephone 2:	Telephone 2:
Email:	Email:	Email:

Name	Name
Address	Address
Telephone 1:	Telephone 1:
Telephone 2:	Telephone 2:
Email:	Email:

The Breed Standard is a written description of the 'perfect' Golden Retriever. Judges use the Breed Standard to evaluate dogs in the show ring.

Name

Address

Telephone 1:

Telephone 2:

Email:

Name

Address

Telephone 1:

Telephone 2:

Email:

Name

Address

Telephone 1:

Telephone 2:

Email:

Name

Address

Telephone 1:

Telephone 2:

Email:

Name

Address

Telephone 1:

Telephone 2:

Email:

Name

Address

Telephone 1:

Telephone 2:

Email:

Name

Address

Telephone 1:

Telephone 2:

Email:

Name

Address

Telephone 1:

Telephone 2:

Email:

Name

Address

Telephone 1:

Telephone 2:

Email:

Name

Address

Telephone 1:

Telephone 2:

Email:

Name

Address

Telephone 1:

Telephone 2:

Email:

Name

Address

Telephone 1:

Telephone 2:

Email:

Name

Address

Telephone 1:

Telephone 2:

Email:

Name

Address

Telephone 1:

Telephone 2:

Email:

Name

Address

Telephone 1:

Telephone 2:

Email:

Name

Address

Telephone 1:

Telephone 2:

Email:

Name

Address

Telephone 1:

Telephone 2:

Email:

In the show ring the Golden Retriever is traditionally 'stacked' in a show pose. The handler holds the dog in position, with its tail out-stretched.

Name

Address

Telephone 1:

Telephone 2:

Email:

Name

Address

Telephone 1:

Telephone 2:

Email:

Name

Address

Telephone 1:

Telephone 2:

Email:

Name

Address

Telephone 1:

Telephone 2:

Email:

Name

Address

Telephone 1:

Telephone 2:

Email:

Name

Address

Telephone 1:

Telephone 2:

Email:

Name

Address

Telephone 1:

Telephone 2:

Email:

Name

Address

Telephone 1:

Telephone 2:

Email:

Name

Address

Telephone 1:

Telephone 2:

Email:

Name	Name	Name
Address	Address	Address
Telephone 1:	Telephone 1:	Telephone 1:
Telephone 2:	Telephone 2:	Telephone 2:
Email:	Email:	Email:
Name	Name	Name
Address	Address	Address
Telephone 1:	Telephone 1:	Telephone 1:
Telephone 2:	Telephone 2:	Telephone 2:
Email:	Email:	Email:
Name	Name	Name
Address	Address	Address
Telephone 1:	Telephone 1:	Telephone 1:
Telephone 2:	Telephone 2:	Telephone 2:
Email:	Email:	Email:

q

Name

Address

Telephone 1:

Telephone 2:

Email:

Name

Address

Telephone 1:

Telephone 2:

Email:

Name

Address

Telephone 1:

Telephone 2:

Email:

Name

Address

Telephone 1:

Telephone 2:

Email:

Name

Address

Telephone 1:

Telephone 2:

Email:

Name

Address

Telephone 1:

Telephone 2:

Email:

Name

Address

Telephone 1:

Telephone 2:

Email:

Name

Address

Telephone 1:

Telephone 2:

Email:

The Golden Retriever is an active, powerful dog, that should appear symmetrical and well balanced.

Name

Address

Telephone 1:

Telephone 2:

Email:

Name

Address

Telephone 1:

Telephone 2:

Email:

Name

Address

Telephone 1:

Telephone 2:

Email:

Name

Address

Telephone 1:

Telephone 2:

Email:

Name

Address

Telephone 1:

Telephone 2:

Email:

Name

Address

Telephone 1:

Telephone 2:

Email:

Name

Address

Telephone 1:

Telephone 2:

Email:

Name

Address

Telephone 1:

Telephone 2:

Email:

Name

Address

Telephone 1:

Telephone 2:

Email:

Name

Address

Telephone 1:

Telephone 2:

Email:

Name

Address

Telephone 1:

Telephone 2:

Email:

Name

Address

Telephone 1:

Telephone 2:

Email:

Name

Address

Telephone 1:

Telephone 2:

Email:

Name

Address

Telephone 1:

Telephone 2:

Email:

Name

Address

Telephone 1:

Telephone 2:

Email:

Name

Address

Telephone 1:

Telephone 2:

Email:

Name

Address

Telephone 1:

Telephone 2:

Email:

Name

Address

Telephone 1:

Telephone 2:

Email:

r

Name

Address

Telephone 1:

Telephone 2:

Email:

Name

Address

Telephone 1:

Telephone 2:

Email:

Name

Address

Telephone 1:

Telephone 2:

Email:

Name

Address

Telephone 1:

Telephone 2:

Email:

Name

Address

Telephone 1:

Telephone 2:

Email:

Name

Address

Telephone 1:

Telephone 2:

Email:

Name

Address

Telephone 1:

Telephone 2:

Email:

Name

Address

Telephone 1:

Telephone 2:

Email:

Goldens are intelligent and biddable, with natural working ability. A kindly expression is a characteristic of the breed.

Name

Address

Telephone 1:

Telephone 2:

Email:

Name

Address

Telephone 1:

Telephone 2:

Email:

Name

Address

Telephone 1:

Telephone 2:

Email:

Name

Address

Telephone 1:

Telephone 2:

Email:

Name

Address

Telephone 1:

Telephone 2:

Email:

Name

Address

Telephone 1:

Telephone 2:

Email:

Name

Address

Telephone 1:

Telephone 2:

Email:

Name

Address

Telephone 1:

Telephone 2:

Email:

Name

Address

Telephone 1:

Telephone 2:

Email:

Name

Address

Telephone 1:

Telephone 2:

Email:

Name

Address

Telephone 1:

Telephone 2:

Email:

Name

Address

Telephone 1:

Telephone 2:

Email:

Name

Address

Telephone 1:

Telephone 2:

Email:

Name

Address

Telephone 1:

Telephone 2:

Email:

Name

Address

Telephone 1:

Telephone 2:

Email:

Name

Address

Telephone 1:

Telephone 2:

Email:

Name

Address

Telephone 1:

Telephone 2:

Email:

When moving, the Golden should have a long free stride, which is powerful and shows good drive.

Name	Name	Name
Address	Address	Address
Telephone 1:	Telephone 1:	Telephone 1:
Telephone 2:	Telephone 2:	Telephone 2:
Email:	Email:	Email:

Name	Name	Name
Address	Address	Address
Telephone 1:	Telephone 1:	Telephone 1:
Telephone 2:	Telephone 2:	Telephone 2:
Email:	Email:	Email:

Name	Name	Name
Address	Address	Address
Telephone 1:	Telephone 1:	Telephone 1:
Telephone 2:	Telephone 2:	Telephone 2:
Email:	Email:	Email:

Name	Name	Name
Address	Address	Address
Telephone 1:	Telephone 1:	Telephone 1:
Telephone 2:	Telephone 2:	Telephone 2:
Email:	Email:	Email:

Name	Name	Name
Address	Address	Address
Telephone 1:	Telephone 1:	Telephone 1:
Telephone 2:	Telephone 2:	Telephone 2:
Email:	Email:	Email:

Name	Name	Name
Address	Address	Address
Telephone 1:	Telephone 1:	Telephone 1:
Telephone 2:	Telephone 2:	Telephone 2:
Email:	Email:	Email:

S

Name

Address

Telephone 1:

Telephone 2:

Email:

Name

Address

Telephone 1:

Telephone 2:

Email:

Name

Address

Telephone 1:

Telephone 2:

Email:

Name

Address

Telephone 1:

Telephone 2:

Email:

Name

Address

Telephone 1:

Telephone 2:

Email:

Name

Address

Telephone 1:

Telephone 2:

Email:

Name

Address

Telephone 1:

Telephone 2:

Email:

Name

Address

Telephone 1:

Telephone 2:

Email:

The coat can be flat or wavy, with feathering. A dense, water-resistant undercoat protects the dog when it is called on to retrieve from cold water.

Name	Name	Name
Address	Address	Address
Telephone 1:	Telephone 1:	Telephone 1:
Telephone 2:	Telephone 2:	Telephone 2:
Email:	Email:	Email:

Name	Name	Name
Address	Address	Address
Telephone 1:	Telephone 1:	Telephone 1:
Telephone 2:	Telephone 2:	Telephone 2:
Email:	Email:	Email:

Name	Name	Name
Address	Address	Address
Telephone 1:	Telephone 1:	Telephone 1:
Telephone 2:	Telephone 2:	Telephone 2:
Email:	Email:	Email:

Name	Name	Name
Address	Address	Address
Telephone 1:	Telephone 1:	Telephone 1:
Telephone 2:	Telephone 2:	Telephone 2:
Email:	Email:	Email:

Name	Name	Name
Address	Address	Address
Telephone 1:	Telephone 1:	Telephone 1:
Telephone 2:	Telephone 2:	Telephone 2:
Email:	Email:	Email:

Name	Name
Address	Address
Telephone 1:	Telephone 1:
Telephone 2:	Telephone 2:
Email:	Email:

In the show ring Golden Retrievers are trimmed to enhance their good points and show the correct outline.

Name	Name	Name
Address	Address	Address
Telephone 1:	Telephone 1:	Telephone 1:
Telephone 2:	Telephone 2:	Telephone 2:
Email:	Email:	Email:

Name	Name	Name
Address	Address	Address
Telephone 1:	Telephone 1:	Telephone 1:
Telephone 2:	Telephone 2:	Telephone 2:
Email:	Email:	Email:

Name	Name	Name
Address	Address	Address
Telephone 1:	Telephone 1:	Telephone 1:
Telephone 2:	Telephone 2:	Telephone 2:
Email:	Email:	Email:

Name		Name		Name	
Address		Address		Address	
Telephone 1:		Telephone 1:		Telephone 1:	
Telephone 2:		Telephone 2:		Telephone 2:	
Email:		Email:		Email:	

Name		Name		Name	
Address		Address		Address	
Telephone 1:		Telephone 1:		Telephone 1:	
Telephone 2:		Telephone 2:		Telephone 2:	
Email:		Email:		Email:	

Name		Name		Name	
Address		Address		Address	
Telephone 1:		Telephone 1:		Telephone 1:	
Telephone 2:		Telephone 2:		Telephone 2:	
Email:		Email:		Email:	

Name	Name	Name
Address	Address	Address
Telephone 1:	Telephone 1:	Telephone 1:
Telephone 2:	Telephone 2:	Telephone 2:
Email:	Email:	Email:

Name	Name	Name
Address	Address	Address
Telephone 1:	Telephone 1:	Telephone 1:
Telephone 2:	Telephone 2:	Telephone 2:
Email:	Email:	Email:

	Name	Name
	Address	Address
	Telephone 1:	Telephone 1:
	Telephone 2:	Telephone 2:
	Email:	Email:

Golden Retrievers in the UK can be any shade of gold or cream. In the show ring, dark coloured dogs, e.g. red or mahogany, are faulted.

Name

Address

Telephone 1:

Telephone 2:

Email:

Name

Address

Telephone 1:

Telephone 2:

Email:

Name

Address

Telephone 1:

Telephone 2:

Email:

Name

Address

Telephone 1:

Telephone 2:

Email:

Name

Address

Telephone 1:

Telephone 2:

Email:

Name

Address

Telephone 1:

Telephone 2:

Email:

Name

Address

Telephone 1:

Telephone 2:

Email:

Name

Address

Telephone 1:

Telephone 2:

Email:

Name

Address

Telephone 1:

Telephone 2:

Email:

Name

Address

Telephone 1:

Telephone 2:

Email:

Name

Address

Telephone 1:

Telephone 2:

Email:

Name

Address

Telephone 1:

Telephone 2:

Email:

Name

Address

Telephone 1:

Telephone 2:

Email:

Name

Address

Telephone 1:

Telephone 2:

Email:

Name

Address

Telephone 1:

Telephone 2:

Email:

Name

Address

Telephone 1:

Telephone 2:

Email:

Name

Address

Telephone 1:

Telephone 2:

Email:

American Golden Retrievers can be a rich, lustrous golden of all shades, but extremely pale dogs are undesirable.

Name

Address

Telephone 1:

Telephone 2:

Email:

Name

Address

Telephone 1:

Telephone 2:

Email:

Name

Address

Telephone 1:

Telephone 2:

Email:

Name

Address

Telephone 1:

Telephone 2:

Email:

Name

Address

Telephone 1:

Telephone 2:

Email:

Name

Address

Telephone 1:

Telephone 2:

Email:

Name

Address

Telephone 1:

Telephone 2:

Email:

Name

Address

Telephone 1:

Telephone 2:

Email:

Name

Address

Telephone 1:

Telephone 2:

Email:

Name	Name	Name
Address	Address	Address
Telephone 1:	Telephone 1:	Telephone 1:
Telephone 2:	Telephone 2:	Telephone 2:
Email:	Email:	Email:

Name	Name	Name
Address	Address	Address
Telephone 1:	Telephone 1:	Telephone 1:
Telephone 2:	Telephone 2:	Telephone 2:
Email:	Email:	Email:

Name	Name	Name
Address	Address	Address
Telephone 1:	Telephone 1:	Telephone 1:
Telephone 2:	Telephone 2:	Telephone 2:
Email:	Email:	Email:

u

Name

Address

Telephone 1:

Telephone 2:

Email:

Name

Address

Telephone 1:

Telephone 2:

Email:

Name

Address

Telephone 1:

Telephone 2:

Email:

Name

Address

Telephone 1:

Telephone 2:

Email:

Name

Address

Telephone 1:

Telephone 2:

Email:

Name

Address

Telephone 1:

Telephone 2:

Email:

Name

Address

Telephone 1:

Telephone 2:

Email:

Name

Address

Telephone 1:

Telephone 2:

Email:

Some Golden Retrievers may have a few white hairs on the chest.

Name	Name	Name
Address	Address	Address
Telephone 1:	Telephone 1:	Telephone 1:
Telephone 2:	Telephone 2:	Telephone 2:
Email:	Email:	Email:

Name	Name	Name
Address	Address	Address
Telephone 1:	Telephone 1:	Telephone 1:
Telephone 2:	Telephone 2:	Telephone 2:
Email:	Email:	Email:

Name	Name	Name
Address	Address	Address
Telephone 1:	Telephone 1:	Telephone 1:
Telephone 2:	Telephone 2:	Telephone 2:
Email:	Email:	Email:

Name

Address

Telephone 1:

Telephone 2:

Email:

Name

Address

Telephone 1:

Telephone 2:

Email:

Name

Address

Telephone 1:

Telephone 2:

Email:

Name

Address

Telephone 1:

Telephone 2:

Email:

Name

Address

Telephone 1:

Telephone 2:

Email:

Name

Address

Telephone 1:

Telephone 2:

Email:

Name

Address

Telephone 1:

Telephone 2:

Email:

Name

Address

Telephone 1:

Telephone 2:

Email:

Name

Address

Telephone 1:

Telephone 2:

Email:

V

Name

Address

Telephone 1:

Telephone 2:

Email:

Name

Address

Telephone 1:

Telephone 2:

Email:

Name

Address

Telephone 1:

Telephone 2:

Email:

Name

Address

Telephone 1:

Telephone 2:

Email:

Name

Address

Telephone 1:

Telephone 2:

Email:

Name

Address

Telephone 1:

Telephone 2:

Email:

Name

Address

Telephone 1:

Telephone 2:

Email:

Name

Address

Telephone 1:

Telephone 2:

Email:

The typical Golden is kindly, friendly, trustworthy and confident, which makes it one of the most popular companion dogs in the world.

Name

Address

Telephone 1:

Telephone 2:

Email:

Name

Address

Telephone 1:

Telephone 2:

Email:

Name

Address

Telephone 1:

Telephone 2:

Email:

Name

Address

Telephone 1:

Telephone 2:

Email:

Name

Address

Telephone 1:

Telephone 2:

Email:

Name

Address

Telephone 1:

Telephone 2:

Email:

Name

Address

Telephone 1:

Telephone 2:

Email:

Name

Address

Telephone 1:

Telephone 2:

Email:

Name

Address

Telephone 1:

Telephone 2:

Email:

Name	Name	Name
Address	Address	Address
Telephone 1:	Telephone 1:	Telephone 1:
Telephone 2:	Telephone 2:	Telephone 2:
Email:	Email:	Email:

Name	Name	Name
Address	Address	Address
Telephone 1:	Telephone 1:	Telephone 1:
Telephone 2:	Telephone 2:	Telephone 2:
Email:	Email:	Email:

Name	Name	Name
Address	Address	Address
Telephone 1:	Telephone 1:	Telephone 1:
Telephone 2:	Telephone 2:	Telephone 2:
Email:	Email:	Email:

W

Name

Address

Telephone 1:

Telephone 2:

Email:

Name

Address

Telephone 1:

Telephone 2:

Email:

Name

Address

Telephone 1:

Telephone 2:

Email:

Name

Address

Telephone 1:

Telephone 2:

Email:

Name

Address

Telephone 1:

Telephone 2:

Email:

Name

Address

Telephone 1:

Telephone 2:

Email:

Name

Address

Telephone 1:

Telephone 2:

Email:

Name

Address

Telephone 1:

Telephone 2:

Email:

The Golden Retriever is popular as a guide dog. The Golden-Labrador Retriever cross has proved the most successful of all the breeds that are used.

Name	Name	Name
Address	Address	Address
Telephone 1:	Telephone 1:	Telephone 1:
Telephone 2:	Telephone 2:	Telephone 2:
Email:	Email:	Email:

Name	Name	Name
Address	Address	Address
Telephone 1:	Telephone 1:	Telephone 1:
Telephone 2:	Telephone 2:	Telephone 2:
Email:	Email:	Email:

Name	Name	Name
Address	Address	Address
Telephone 1:	Telephone 1:	Telephone 1:
Telephone 2:	Telephone 2:	Telephone 2:
Email:	Email:	Email:

Name

Address

Telephone 1:

Telephone 2:

Email:

Name

Address

Telephone 1:

Telephone 2:

Email:

Name

Address

Telephone 1:

Telephone 2:

Email:

Name

Address

Telephone 1:

Telephone 2:

Email:

Name

Address

Telephone 1:

Telephone 2:

Email:

Name

Address

Telephone 1:

Telephone 2:

Email:

Name

Address

Telephone 1:

Telephone 2:

Email:

Name

Address

Telephone 1:

Telephone 2:

Email:

The gentle, biddable nature of the Golden makes it ideally suited to work as an assistance dog, helping people with a variety of disabilities.

Name	Name	Name
Address	Address	Address
Telephone 1:	Telephone 1:	Telephone 1:
Telephone 2:	Telephone 2:	Telephone 2:
Email:	Email:	Email:

Name	Name	Name
Address	Address	Address
Telephone 1:	Telephone 1:	Telephone 1:
Telephone 2:	Telephone 2:	Telephone 2:
Email:	Email:	Email:

Name	Name	Name
Address	Address	Address
Telephone 1:	Telephone 1:	Telephone 1:
Telephone 2:	Telephone 2:	Telephone 2:
Email:	Email:	Email:

Name

Address

Telephone 1:

Telephone 2:

Email:

Name

Address

Telephone 1:

Telephone 2:

Email:

Name

Address

Telephone 1:

Telephone 2:

Email:

Name

Address

Telephone 1:

Telephone 2:

Email:

Name

Address

Telephone 1:

Telephone 2:

Email:

Name

Address

Telephone 1:

Telephone 2:

Email:

Name

Address

Telephone 1:

Telephone 2:

Email:

Name

Address

Telephone 1:

Telephone 2:

Email:

Name

Address

Telephone 1:

Telephone 2:

Email:

x y z

Name

Address

Telephone 1:

Telephone 2:

Email:

Name

Address

Telephone 1:

Telephone 2:

Email:

Name

Address

Telephone 1:

Telephone 2:

Email:

Name

Address

Telephone 1:

Telephone 2:

Email:

Name

Address

Telephone 1:

Telephone 2:

Email:

Name

Address

Telephone 1:

Telephone 2:

Email:

Name

Address

Telephone 1:

Telephone 2:

Email:

Name

Address

Telephone 1:

Telephone 2:

Email:

Doc, an avalanche rescue dog, saved Jeff Eckland from under 5 ft of snow in Kirkwood Ski Resort California. Jeff now has a tattoo of Doc on his chest.

Name	Name	Name
Address	Address	Address
Telephone 1:	Telephone 1:	Telephone 1:
Telephone 2:	Telephone 2:	Telephone 2:
Email:	Email:	Email:
Name	Name	Name
Address	Address	Address
Telephone 1:	Telephone 1:	Telephone 1:
Telephone 2:	Telephone 2:	Telephone 2:
Email:	Email:	Email:
Name	Name	Name
Address	Address	Address
Telephone 1:	Telephone 1:	Telephone 1:
Telephone 2:	Telephone 2:	Telephone 2:
Email:	Email:	Email:

Name

Address

Telephone 1:

Telephone 2:

Email:

Name

Address

Telephone 1:

Telephone 2:

Email:

Name

Address

Telephone 1:

Telephone 2:

Email:

Name

Address

Telephone 1:

Telephone 2:

Email:

Name

Address

Telephone 1:

Telephone 2:

Email:

Name

Address

Telephone 1:

Telephone 2:

Email:

Name

Address

Telephone 1:

Telephone 2:

Email:

Name

Address

Telephone 1:

Telephone 2:

Email:

How many dogs does it take to change a light bulb?
Golden: "The sun is shining, we've got our whole lives ahead of us, and you're worrying about a bulb?"